The Emperor's New Clothes

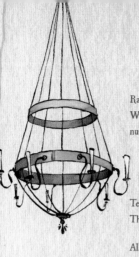

Raintree is an imprint of Capstone Global Library Limited, a company incorporated in England and
Wales having its registered office at 264 Banbury Road, Oxford, OX2 7DY – Registered company
number: 6695582

www.raintree.co.uk
myorders@raintree.co.uk

Edited by Gina Kammer
Designed by Bob Lentz
Original illustrations © Capstone Global Library Limited 2020
Production by Michelle Biedscheid
Originated by Capstone Global Library Ltd

978 1 4747 9147 2

British Library Cataloguing in Publication Data
A full catalogue record for this book is available from the British Library.

All the internet addresses (URLs) given in this book were valid at the time of going to press.
However, due to the dynamic nature of the internet, some addresses may have changed, or sites
may have changed or ceased to exist since publication. While the author and publisher regret
any inconvenience this may cause readers, no responsibility for any such changes can be
accepted by either the author or the publisher.

Printed and bound in India.

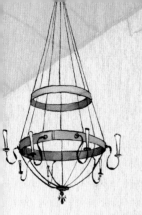
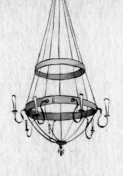
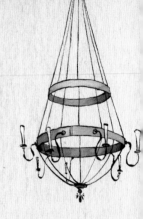

HANS CHRISTIAN ANDERSEN'S

The Emperor's New Clothes

THE GRAPHIC NOVEL

retold by
Stephanie True Peters

illustrated by
Jeffrey Stewart Timmins

raintree 🍃

a Capstone company — publishers for children

Cast of Characters

THE SWINDLERS

THE TREASURER

THE BOY

THE EMPEROR

THE SERVANT

Long ago in a faraway land, there lived an emperor who prized fancy clothes above all else.

These are delightful!

Send the tailor of these fine garments a sack of gold coins!

Yes, your Highness!

The emperor's wardrobe took up an entire wing of his castle.

Rulers of other kingdoms inspected their soldiers.

Excellent! I've never seen a finer group in my life!

The emperor, however, inspected new hats.

Excellent! I've never seen a finer group in my life!

Other leaders ordered improvements to their kingdoms.

Put a bridge there and spare no expense!

Very good, your Majesty!

The emperor, however, ordered improvements to his footwear.

Put a buckle there and spare no expense!

Very good, your Highness!

Other kings visited their villages so they could see their subjects.

It's so good to see you again!

Thank you, Sire!

But the emperor visited his village so his subjects could see him in his latest outfit.

It's so good for you to see me again!

One day, the emperor was riding through the village market . . .

What do you think of this cloth, Sire?

Don't be silly. It is far too plain for a king to wear.

Yes, your Highness.

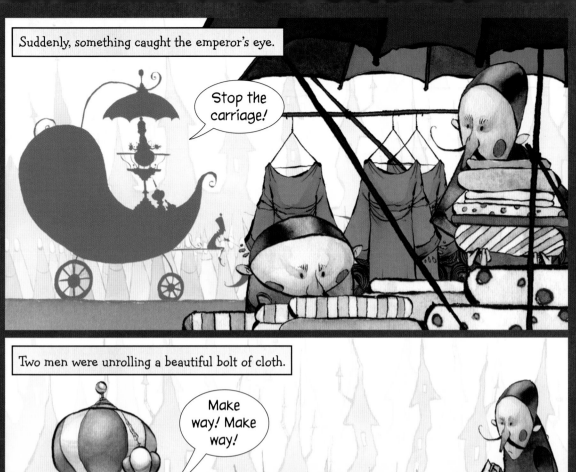

Suddenly, something caught the emperor's eye.

Stop the carriage!

Two men were unrolling a beautiful bolt of cloth.

Make way! Make way!

The emperor was delighted with the cloth that he saw.

Such fine work! You are truly expert weavers!

Thank you, your Highness.

Yes, thank you.

But in truth, the men were not weavers. They were swindlers.

They had heard the emperor adored fancy clothes.

The emperor will spend his entire fortune on new garments!

All the better for me!

And perhaps better for us, too!

So they came up with a plan to trick the emperor out of his treasure.

This cloth will make a fine new suit!

A new suit is indeed fine . . .

. . . but wouldn't you like something extraordinary?

I will provide you with a place to weave.

When the magical cloth is complete, you will make it into a suit for me.

If only it didn't take so much energy to make this cloth.

You shall have plenty of food and drink to give you strength!

Ah, how gracious of you, Sire.

Yes, but our magic cloth is also very expensive to make.

Then you shall have all the money you need!

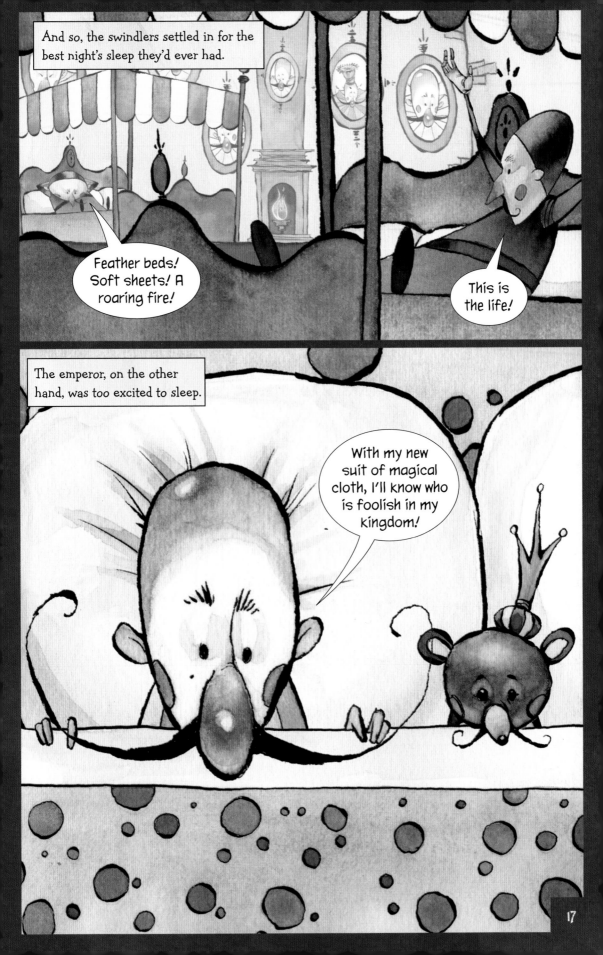

The weavers' supplies arrived early the next morning.

Are these looms to your liking?

We had expected better . . .

. . . but they will have to do.

Hmmm. Will this be enough thread?

Goodness, no! We'll need twice as much!

I shall see to it at once!

13

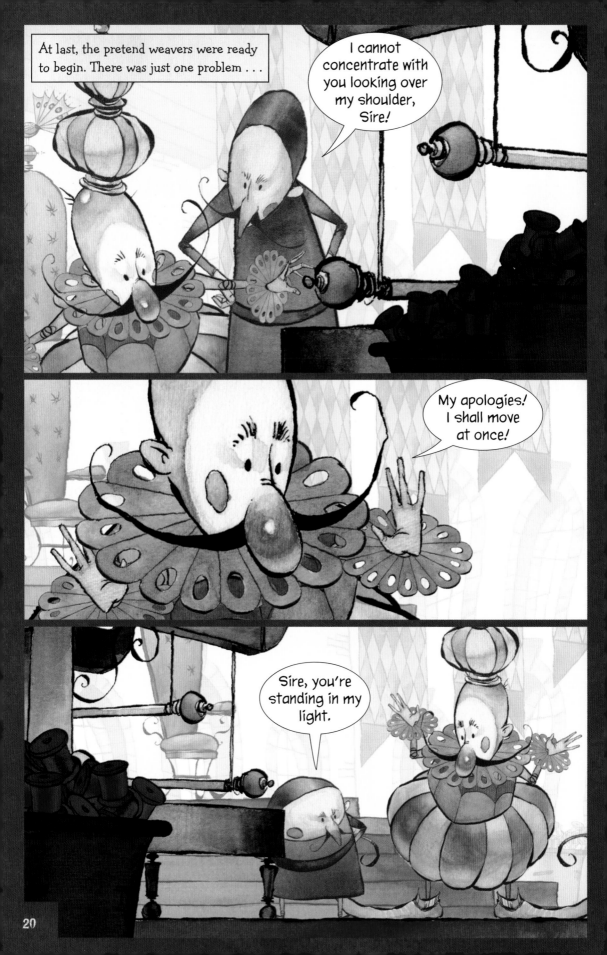

21

While the emperor waited, a frightful thought occurred to him.

Oh, no!

TAP!
TAP!

What if I'm not clever enough to see the magic cloth?

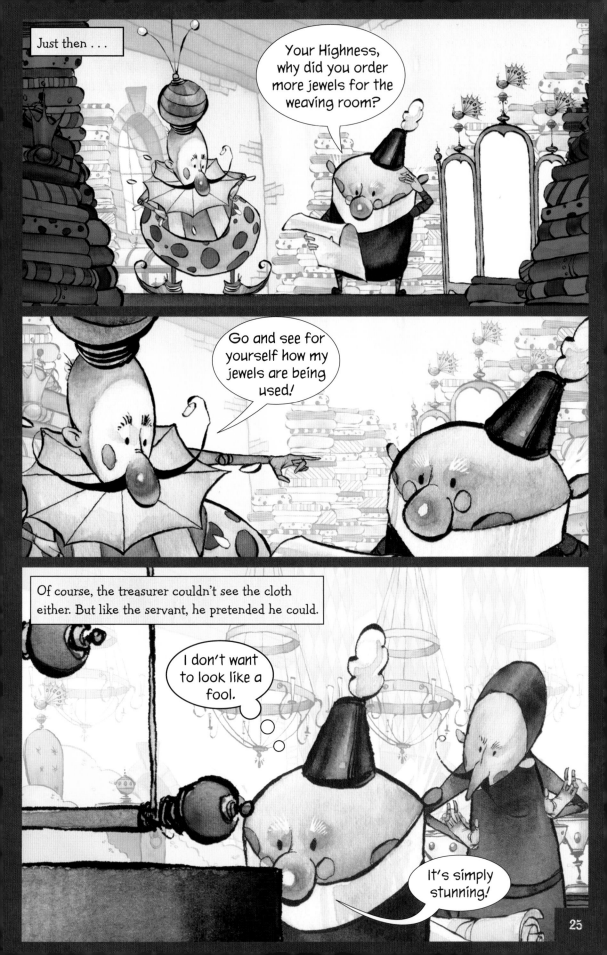

He peered inside to see . . .

. . . two weavers, two empty looms — and nothing more!

Your Highness, you are just in time!

As you can *clearly* see, we have finished weaving!

Of course, the emperor couldn't see the cloth at all. But he knew better than to say so!

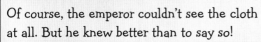

See how it shimmers!

So soft! So delicate!

It looks exactly like I imagined it! Begin my suit at once!

27

The weavers worked all day . . .

. . . and into the night.

Until at last, the emperor's new clothes were finished.

You look magnificent, Sire!

You simply must let everyone see you in your marvellous new suit!

Indeed! I shall hold a grand procession in the village tomorrow!

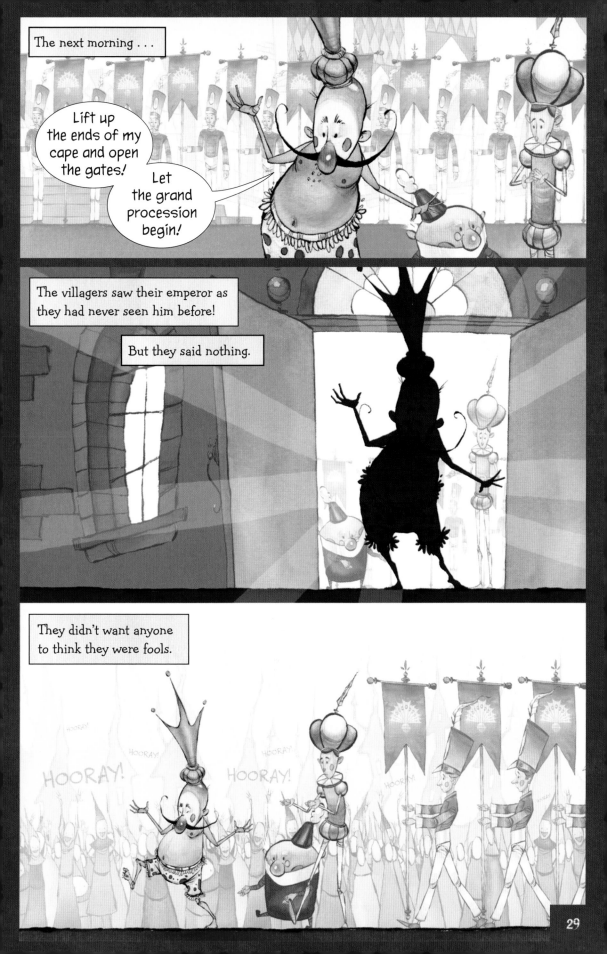

The next morning . . .

Lift up the ends of my cape and open the gates!

Let the grand procession begin!

The villagers saw their emperor as they had never seen him before!

But they said nothing.

They didn't want anyone to think they were fools.

HOORAY!

HOORAY!

The emperor was quite pleased with the crowd's reaction.

Until . . .

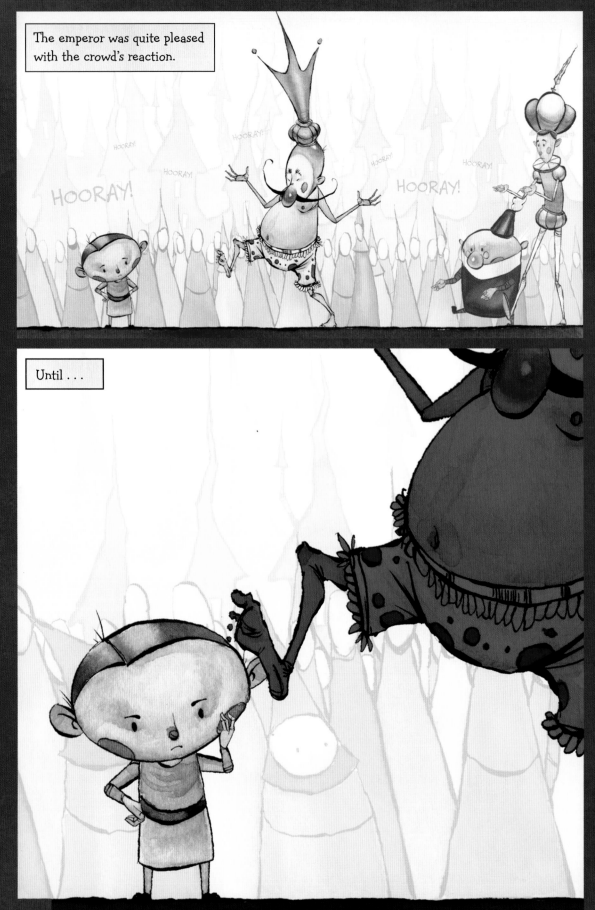

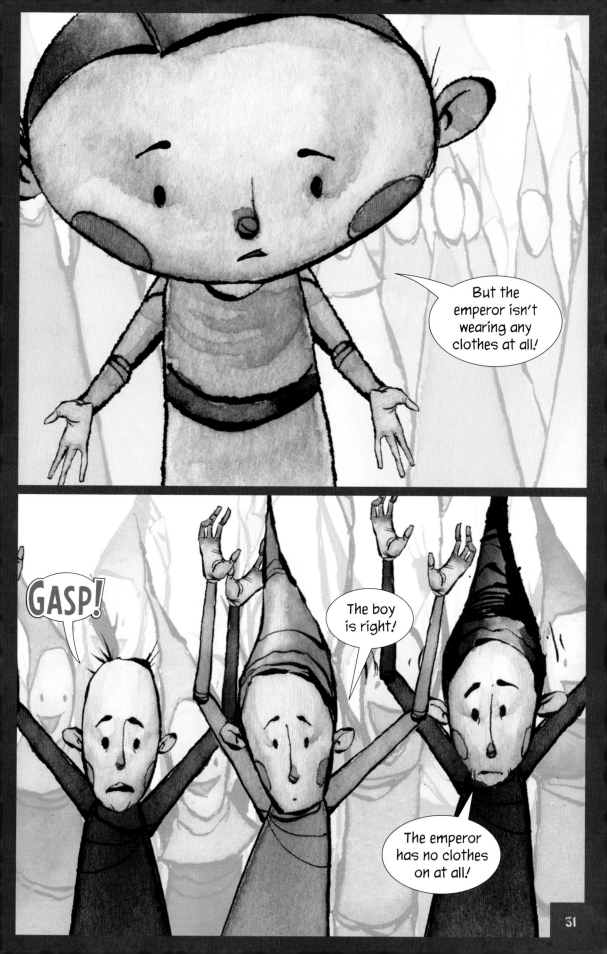

And the swindlers? They gave up their life of crime . . .

. . . at least until they had spent all of the emperor's treasure!

Where to next, partner?

Wherever we can part a fool from his money!

glossary

ADORN decorate or add beauty to something

ATTIRE clothing

DELICATE finely made and fragile

GARMENTS pieces of clothing

INSISTED demanded something

INSPECTED looked at something very carefully

PROCESSION number of people walking along as part of a parade

SHIMMERS shines with a faint, steady light

SIRE respectful term of address for a male ruler

SUBJECTS people who live in a kingdom under the rule of a king or queen

WARDROBE collection of clothes belonging to one person

about the author

Hans Christian Andersen was born in Odense, Denmark, on 2 April 1805. As Hans grew up, he tried many different professions, but none seemed to fit. He eventually found work as an actor and singer, but when his voice changed, he could no longer sing well enough to make a living. Then, a friend suggested that he start writing. A short time later, he published his first story, "The Ghost at Palnatoke's Grave".

Andersen's first book of fairy tales was published in 1835. He continued to write children's stories, publishing one almost every year, until he fell ill in 1872. Andersen had written more than 150 fairy tales before his death in 1875. He is considered to be the father of the modern fairy tale.

about the retelling author

After working for more than 10 years as a children's book editor, Stephanie True Peters started writing books herself. She has since written 40 books, including the New York Times best seller "A Princess Primer: A Fairy Godmother's Guide to Being a Princess". When not at her computer, Stephanie enjoys playing with her two children, going to the gym or working on DIY with her patient and supportive husband, Daniel.

about the illustrator

Jeffrey Stewart Timmins was born on 2 July 1979. In 2003, he graduated from the Classical Animation course at Sheridan College in Ontario, Canada. He currently works as a freelance designer and animator. Even as an adult, Timmins still holds onto a few important items from his childhood, such as his rubber boots, cape and lensless sunglasses.

discussion questions

1. Why do you think it took so long for someone to point out that the emperor wasn't wearing any clothes?

2. Emperors are chosen by birth. Presidents and Prime Ministers are chosen by elections. Which way of choosing a leader do you think is better? Why?

3. If the swindlers were caught, what do you think would be a fair punishment for them? Prison? A fine? Something else?

writing prompts

1. Imagine that you're an emperor. What laws would you
   make? Would you be a strict and stern ruler, or a kind
   and caring ruler? Write about your kingdom.

2. The swindlers make money by tricking other people.
   Have you ever been tricked? What did you do about it?
   How did it make you feel?

3. At the end of the book, the swindlers ran out of money.
   Do you think it was wise to spend it so quickly?
   What would you have done with all that wealth?

FIND OUT MORE

The book may be over, but the adventure is just beginning.

Would you like to find out more about traditional and reimagined fairy tales and stories? Then check out these websites!

pookpress.co.uk/project/fairy-tales-from-around-the-world
Discover new fairy tales from around the world, and learn more about the authors and history behind some of the most famous fairy tales.

roalddahl.com/create-and-learn/write
Pick up some great tips for creating and writing your own stories.

storyberries.com
Read and listen to traditional and reimagined fairy tales and poems.